Piano Exam Pieces

ABRSM Grade 1

Selected from the 2017 & 2018 syllabus

Name

Date of ex

GW00368104

© 2016 by The Associated Board of the Royal Schools of Music

Contents

Editor for ABRSM: Richard Jones

Other pieces for Grade 1

First published in 2016 by ABRSM (Publishing) Ltd,
a wholly owned subsidiary of ABRSM, 24 Portland Place,
London W1B 1LU, United Kingdom
© 2016 by The Associated Board of the Royal Schools of Music
Distributed worldwide by Oxford University Press

Music origination by Julia Bovee
Cover by Kate Benjamin & Andy Potts
Printed in England by Halstan & Co. Ltd, Amersham,
Bucks., on materials from sustainable sources.
Reprinted in 2016

Aria in F

BWV Anh. II 131

J. C. Bach
(1735–82)

This charming little piece was written by Bach's youngest son Johann Christian when he was little more than 10 years old. He wrote it out in the *Clavierbüchlein*, or Little Keyboard Book, that Bach dedicated to his wife Anna Magdalena in 1725. This manuscript album, filled up gradually over the next 20 years or so, gives a vivid picture of domestic music-making in the Bach family home during that period.

The wedges in b. 4 etc. denote staccato and imply a light accent. Minims so marked might be shortened to half their value. The dynamics are editorial suggestions only, as are the slurs and staccatos, except for the right-hand wedges in bb. 12 and 14.

Source: Staatsbibliothek zu Berlin, Preußischer Kulturbesitz, Mus.ms.Bach P225

© 2016 by The Associated Board of the Royal Schools of Music
Adapted from J. S. Bach et al.: *The Anna Magdalena Bach Book of 1725*, edited by Richard Jones (ABRSM)

Canaries

A:2

Arranged by Sarah Watts

Anon.

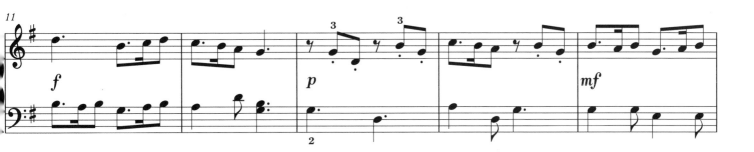

Imagine a quick dance with lots of jumping and stamping of feet! As its name suggests, the *canarie* originally came from the Canary Islands, but it spread to Spain in the 1500s and then France in the 1600s.

  Canaries is a French lute piece from the Straloch Lutebook (Aberdeen, 1627). This collection was compiled by Robert Graham (1580–1661) of Straloch, Scotland. It contains many pieces of French as well as Scottish origin.

The woman is fickle

La donna è mobile

from *Rigoletto*

Giuseppe Verdi
(1813–1901)

Arranged by Nancy Litten

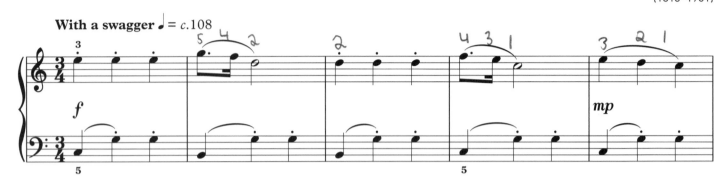

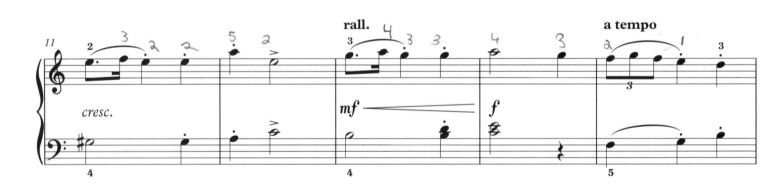

This is a piano arrangement of a famous tenor aria from Act III of Verdi's *Rigoletto*. This opera was composed in 1851 and first performed in Venice later in the same year. In 'La donna è mobile', the Duke of Mantua declares that women are changeable in their affections.

Bouncing Billy

from *Take Your Pick*

B:1

Joan Last
(1908–2002)

This dance-like tune is shared between the hands (the middle C in b. 2, for example, belongs to the theme). From the upbeat to b. 17, a new theme is heard in alternating hands. Finally, at b. 26 the original theme returns, now with the surprise of a chromatic, *poco stringendo* conclusion (that is, gradually getting a little faster).

Joan Last was an English musician who taught the piano for many years at the Royal Academy of Music, London.

B:2

Gypsy Song

No. 6 from *A Baker's Dozen*

Bryan Kelly
(born 1934)

This piece begins with a haunting melody in the style of a folk song (bb. 1–8). After a contrasting middle section (bb. 9–16), the melody returns in the bass, with an accompanying part in the treble (bb. 17–26). Notice here how the left- and right-hand phrases overlap.

Bryan Kelly studied at the Royal College of Music, London, and with Nadia Boulanger in Paris. He has taught at both the Royal Scottish Academy of Music and Drama (now the Royal Conservatoire of Scotland) and the Royal College of Music.

In the Distant Forest

Dans la forêt lointaine

B:3

arranged by Hywel Davies

Trad. French

Allegretto [♩ = *c*.100]

marcato

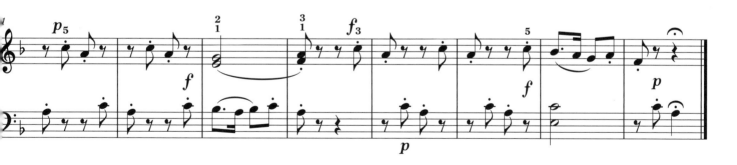

The first two lines of this traditional French song are as follows:

Dans la forêt lointaine,   In the distant forest,
On entend le coucou.   You can hear the cuckoo.

In this arrangement, the cuckoo is first heard in the right hand and echoed in the left (bb. 9–10), then heard in the left and echoed in the right (bb. 13–14). Composer Hywel Davies is known for his arrangements of folk music, such as those included in the *Folk Roots* series published by Boosey & Hawkes.

Asian Tiger Prowl

Rob Hall
(born 1969)

The composer has written: 'The image is of a tiger homing in on its prey, pausing at times, and pouncing at the end. Close attention to the articulation markings will reveal the tiger's true character. The piece is based on the D natural minor scale, or Aeolian mode. Originating from Asia Minor, the mode is used in western music, including jazz, but also features in the raga music of northern India – a home of tigers!'

Saxophonist and clarinettist Rob Hall has written for a range of ensembles with commissions from chamber choirs to jazz orchestras. With numerous CD releases and new publications of his music, this versatility is mirrored in his role as a jazz and classical examiner with ABRSM.

Скакалка Skakalka

Skipping Rope

No. 1 from *Children's Album*, Book 2

C:2

Aram Khachaturian
(1903–78)

This musical picture of a skipping rope in action is selected from Khachaturian's *Children's Album* (Детский альбом Detskii al'bom), of which the first volume appeared in 1946 and the second in 1964. The opening melody occurs three times. Its first and third statements (bb. 1 and 17) are virtually identical, but the middle one (b. 9) is quieter, in the dominant key, and has a legato, chromatic accompaniment in the left hand. The left-hand *a* on the fourth beat of b. 16 belongs to the tune (compare the upbeat to b. 1) and so needs a little emphasis.

Aram Khachaturian studied at the Gnesin Institute, Moscow (1922–9) and then at the Moscow Conservatory (1929–36). He later taught at both institutions. His colourful, pictorial compositions include three symphonies, three concertos, film music and ballets, notably Spartacus, which has become his most famous work.

C:3

When the saints go marching in

Arranged by Kenneth Bartels

Trad. America

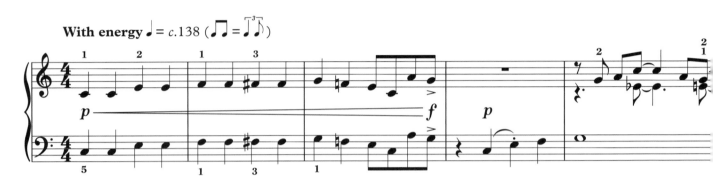

'When the saints go marching in' is an American gospel hymn. It is often played by jazz bands, so the jazzy style of this piano arrangement, with swung quavers, is well suited to it. The lyrics begin as follows:

Oh when the saints go marching in,
Oh when the saints go marching in,
Lord, I want to be in that number,
When the saints go marching in.